FROM SIDCUP WITH PURRS

The Story of a Small Cat with a Big Personality

HEATHER COOK

PHOTOGRAPHS BY ROGER COOK

Matador
9 Priory Business Park,
Wistow Road, Kibworth Beauchamp,
Leicestershire. LE8 0RX
Tel: (+44) 116 279 2299
Fax: (+44) 116 279 2277
Email: books@troubador.co.uk
Web: www.troubador.co.uk/matador

ISBN 978 1783065 547

British Library Cataloguing in Publication Data.
A catalogue record for this book is available from the British Library.

Typeset in 12pt Book Antiqua by Troubador Publishing Ltd, Leicester, UK
Printed and bound in the UK by TJ International, Padstow, Cornwall

Matador is an imprint of Troubador Publishing Ltd

For Poor Roger, who suffers so nobly and who was brave enough to come into my life and stick around – probably because he fell hopelessly in love with my very special cats

INTRODUCTION

I don't remember much about my kittenhood and perhaps it's just as well. I must have had a home of sorts, but it couldn't have been a very good one or I wouldn't have found myself on the streets at an early age. There were good things, like pigeons to chase and leftover takeaways, but there were plenty of bad things, like hungry foxes and horrible yobs who threw things at me and tried to kick me.

Anyway, I've always been the girl for a challenge and, although I say it myself, I was a plucky little number as well as being quite amazingly beautiful. I soon got to grips with the best places to hang out to grab the juiciest goodies; Kentucky Fried Chicken was pretty good, but the Chinese takeaways were always covered in some sticky muck that stuck to my fur and tasted like kitten poo.

One day, a woman saw me dragging a chicken leg behind a dustbin and walked towards me, calling out in that special voice that some people think cats find beguiling. Luckily, I couldn't really grasp what she was saying because I'm quite hard of hearing, but what I did catch was pretty alarming.

'You poor little scrap!' she cooed, 'you must be desperately hungry to eat that rotten old chicken! Come here – there's nothing to be afraid of!'

Yeah, right. She obviously wanted the chicken for herself. No way was I falling for that old trick and wriggled as far back as I could into the smelly shadows. After a while, the cooing stopped and I crept out. There was no sign of the woman, so I assumed she must have gone to find her own bit of chicken somewhere else.

In my trusting way, I reckoned without the innate cunning of even a fairly stupid member of the human race. A couple of days later, I turned up by my favourite dustbin and found some fresh juicy pieces of chicken on the ground. Yippee! I grasped the biggest one and ducked behind the bin to wolf it down, then emerged to grab another bit. Within seconds, someone had caught hold of me by the scruff of the neck and shoved me in a box. It was that woman – the one that had been getting on my nerves with that irritating cooing.

'There we are! Nothing to worry about! I'm going to take you to my lovely vet – he'll know what to do. My Beauty swears by him.'

If the old bat thought I'd find this reassuring, she was even dafter than I'd thought. She might just as well have said that she was taking me to see a cat-murderer and be done with it. The only thing that cheered me up was piddling copiously on her lap as we lurched along on a smelly old bus. I can't tell you how thrilled she was as it seeped through the gaps in the cat carrier, but she remained relentlessly cheerful, which was annoying.

'Poor pussy's scared of the noisy old bus!' she explained to her horrified fellow-travellers. 'She doesn't know it's all for her own good!'

I was so outraged by the woman's complacent twittering that I chucked up the recently consumed chicken, achieving a spectacular waterfall effect through the front of the box.

Eventually, we arrived at the unbelievably wonderful vet's surgery and my "rescuer" lifted me up for inspection.

'I'm afraid we're not looking our best,' she explained – and she certainly wasn't with all that sick congealing on her red coat and a large wet patch covering most of her front. 'I couldn't think where else to take the poor little thing. I couldn't possibly leave her in that dreadful car park and you know that my Beauty would never tolerate another cat in our tiny flat.'

With these encouraging words, Beauty's mother cleared off, leaving me face to face with a child of twelve. He was, allegedly, a highly qualified veterinary surgeon, but I kept expecting his mother to appear at any moment, demanding to know why he'd left his bedroom in such a mess.

So that was how I arrived at a veterinary surgery in a place called Sidcup, where my old worries were rapidly replaced by new ones and I began to realise there was more to life than Kentucky Fried Chicken – I just wasn't sure what.

CHAPTER ONE

The Sidcup Years

'Considerable brain damage and a significant head-tilt,' observed the child who indeed turned out to be a vet. I was surprised, because I thought you had to be quite bright to be a vet and I hadn't noticed anything unusual about his head, although now he came to mention it...

'And she seems to have some hearing problems too. Pity – she's a pretty little thing, but realistically I can't see too many people clamouring to give her a home.'

Clunk! The penny dropped; he was talking about me! Bloody cheek. For a moment being even harder of hearing seemed like an attractive option because I could have done without knowing what he thought. After the child vet and his even younger assistant had finished pulling me about, they put me into a cage thing with a bowl of food. In one corner there was a plastic tray with bits in which anybody in their right mind would assume was a bed and in another there was a scrunched up blanket, which by process of elimination – if you'll pardon the pun – had to be the toilet. Having cleared the plate and made myself comfortable, I dropped off, only to be disturbed by the toddler assistant opening the cage and carrying on about the smell as she scooped up the blanket.

'That's not for pooing in!' she twittered, 'that's your bed, you silly pussycat. You should do your poosies in the tray!'

1

I looked at her in astonishment and went straight back to sleep.

After a while they let me out of the cage and stood there staring at me while I tore round the room, batting some screwed up paper around. I noticed that some of the other cages were occupied by animals wearing some pretty trendy accessories. One fuzzy little dog was sporting a white lampshade, which he bashed against the side of the cage in a rather listless manner, and a bored-looking ginger cat had a hind leg encased in a bright blue elastic stocking. If the humans thought I'd be unnerved by the sight of these two, they were spot on. Were they carrying out experiments on these innocent victims? Would I be next in line? Would I end up with two tails, or some other modification too terrifying to contemplate?

They decided to call me "Tiny". This momentous decision was only reached after considerable discussion, culminating in a vote between "Tiny", "Hyacinth" and "Pudding Chops", so there was much to be thankful for. They wasted a lot of time worrying about what I'd been called in my previous home, but I could have told them the list was endless and included, "Bloodycat", "Clearoff" and "Wasteofspace".

Time passed and I began to feel more confident as the other occupants of the steel cages came and went. It seemed that Professor Child-Vet and his cronies were engaged in patching up dogs and cats that had come to grief, before releasing them into the care of their besotted owners. For a while they thought a grief-stricken owner might be looking for me, but I could have told them that they were whistling in the wind there. The last thing I wanted to see coming through the door was the gang of misfits that had made my early life such a misery.

The Professor couldn't resist sticking needles in me and shoving foul-smelling stuff on the back of my neck, but in his clumsy way he was kind and the food was good. I used to be banged up in the cage during surgery hours as they said I was a danger to myself and other animals! Me! Just because I made it my business to befriend the terrified creatures in the waiting room, the humans decided that I had no survival instincts and took this absence of fear to be evidence of brain damage. Where this line of thinking leaves the other heroines of history, such as Joan of Arc and Boadicea, I have no idea.

Another theory was that I suffered from delusions of grandeur and wanted to rule the world. There was me thinking I was doing this slobbery old Labrador a favour by cosying up to him, but their version was that I frightened the great lump and forced him to seek refuge under the chair. It was hardly my fault if the stupid mutt overturned the chair – and his owner – in the process.

In due course, the toddler assistant came skipping into work with the joyous news that she had found a home for me and a few days later I was on my way. Within hours, I was brought back in disgrace for "inappropriate toileting". For God's sake! What's a bit of poo between friends!

Over the next few months, I perfected the art of escaping and succeeded in making several spirited dashes to the nursery next door. The children were very pleased to see me, but this boundless enthusiasm was not universal and I was carted back by grim-faced women who burbled endlessly about germs and parasites. They needn't have worried – I wasn't bothered about catching anything from the children and I didn't notice any fleas scampering across their pudgy little faces.

I was sent home with another woman who promised much, but surprisingly she cut up rough when I broke some hideous ornament which had been left to her in her aunt's Will. I can only say that Auntie must have really hated her to force a rat-faced shepherdess on to the poor woman. Not that she was grateful to me, but she certainly should have been.

Back I came to the vet's surgery and life settled back into its normal pattern, enlivened by the occasional foray into the waiting room or an escape to the nursery next door. Things could have been a lot worse, but I really didn't like that cage and, to be fair to her, the kind-hearted toddler didn't like putting me in there.

Meanwhile, unbeknown to her and to me, a conversation was taking place over lunch in a school in Essex. Three people were munching their way through a jacket potato (no – they didn't actually have to share – they had one each) before subjecting some unsuspecting children to a talk about cats.

One of the trio, a boring-looking middle-aged woman with a face like a melon and tufts of tortoiseshell hair, was droning on about her "Special Needs" cats while the other two yawned and poked wearily at the remains of their lunch.

'Yes, they're all very needy pussycats in one way or another,' she wittered.

The second member of the threesome, a younger, brighter woman, smiled politely; realising that more was expected of her, she rashly enquired as to the nature of the

"Special Needs" and immediately regretted doing so, losing the will to live as the tufty one meandered on about her cats – few of whom appeared to have the full complement of limbs or indeed any other bits.

The third person present, a kindly young man who seemed dangerously normal, suddenly burst into life.

'The cat I feel really sorry for is Tiny,' he said. 'You know my wife's a vet in Sidcup? Well, this poor little cat has lived at the surgery for nearly three years now and she has to spend quite a bit of time in a cage because of her disabilities.'

'Disabilities?' asked the melon-faced woman tremulously, 'what sort of disabilities?'

'She's got some brain damage,' replied the young man, 'which means she knows no fear and launches herself at other animals even if they're aggressive. She has a head-tilt and is quite deaf too, so she can't be allowed to roam freely.'

'She sounds like the sort of pussycat that should come and live with us!' shrieked the weird woman. 'Not that it matters, but what colour is she?'

'Tabby – I'm sure my wife said she was tabby,' gibbered the man, hardly able to believe his luck and almost eating his plastic fork in his excitement. 'Did I mention that she has some toileting problems? Misses the dirt tray sometimes...'

By this time, old Melon-Chops was past caring about a few dirt tray mishaps; she was a woman with a mission, and that mission was little old me.

Apparently, on returning home she decided not to mention anything about this latest project to her long-suffering husband, preferring to wait for the right moment.

I suspect that the poor man could have seen through this pathetic plan in a darkened room with both eyes closed, but playing these little games had provided the woman with much innocent amusement over the years.

The "right moment" came when – by way of a change – the happy couple had been whiling away a couple of hours at Cats Protection Headquarters. As usual they had punished themselves by looking at the waifs and strays available for adoption and the cunning woman had noticed how taken her husband was with a pretty little tabby girl.

On the way home she asked him which cat he would have chosen, if they had been looking for another cat.

'The little tabby,' he replied. 'I'd love to have another tabby.'

Game, set and match to the fat old witch with the tortoiseshell hair.

The first indication that my life might be about to change was a spate of activity in the surgery. My vaccination certificate was dusted off and a worm pill shoved down my throat ahead of schedule. The toddler assistant and the rest of the gang cuddled me more often than usual and kept saying alarming things like, 'we'll miss you terribly, Tiny, but it's all for the best!'

I was asleep in my cage when they appeared. For a while I thought I was having one of those funny waking dreams – if only! There was a dumpy woman with wild tufty hair and a slightly more normal looking man and they were staring at me and doing all that blinking stuff that humans think cats find reassuring. I can tell you that with the sunlight glancing off those spectacles it was positively terrifying.

Unsurprisingly, they were entranced with me and soon I was on my way to a new life. I've since realised that they would have been entranced with a fur-covered slug, but at the time I felt flattered. Little did I know what awaited me at Tresta Towers! It was like *The Rocky Horror Show* with cats.

CHAPTER TWO

Unpromising Material

For goodness sake! I could only think there must have been an end of season sale or some terrible disaster with Woking as its epicentre. When we arrived, the humans shoved me into a cage thing and forced me to watch a procession of the weirdest cats I'd ever clapped eyes on. Most of them had bits missing, or were just insane, but either way it was a pretty scary experience. Back in Sidcup, the recovery room often resembled a war zone, but it was worse here because there was no indication that these poor creatures were ever going to get better.

After a few days they let me out of the pen and I launched myself at the fat ginger thing known as Benjamin Wobble. I can't tell you how satisfactory it was, rolling him over and chewing at that porky little body! He was squeaking away when the Earth Mother, as old Melon-Chops seemed to be known, swooped on me and banged me up in the cage. She picked up the ginger lump and cuddled him.

'I can't believe what that naughty girl did to poor Benjy!' she wittered, smoothing his ruffled fur. 'She's a *very* bad girl indeed and I think we'll have to take her back to Sidcup!'

Oh well – see if I care! They needn't have thought I would be blackmailed into behaving myself. Anyway, they didn't take me back to Sidcup, so that was all a load of rubbish.

Another worry was that some silly old white cat with three legs decided she couldn't possibly walk past my cage, so she stayed out all night causing a terrible upset.

'Supposing Whizzy leaves home?' droned the Earth Mother to the long-suffering man known as Poor Roger. 'She seems really frightened of little Tiny! Why can't they all love each other?'

Because we're cats, Dummy! And because we've got minds of our own – even the ones with bits missing. Okay, I had pulled some pretty frightening faces at the old tart as she hopped up to the patio door; it's surprising what you can do with tabby stripes, and whatever I did certainly terrified old Whizzy-Pops!

After several nights of Whizzy opting for the wilder side of life, the EM and Poor Roger couldn't stand it any longer and decided that a new plan was called for. They engaged Count Lucio in conversation, which was the equivalent of trying to teach a dinosaur to play chess. Count Lucio was an enormous black cat with a brain the size of a particularly small pea and his enthusiasm for engaging in any sort of conversation – meaningful or not – waned as soon as he realised it didn't involve food or slapping foxes (a favourite hobby of his).

'We're only suggesting this because we think you're the sort of cat who can see the bigger picture,' said Poor Roger, unhooking the Count's massive front paws from his neck as beads of blood oozed through. 'The thing is that little Tiny needs a room of her own where Whizzy can't see her, because Whizzy is very fritted – sorry, frightened – of the new girl and won't come in at night.' I had already noticed that the EM and Poor Roger tended to lapse into "Benjy-Speak" under emotional pressure; this was how they imagined dear little Benjy would speak if he could and if you are looking for some rational thought process, I would advise giving up at an early stage because there isn't one.

The EM joined in. 'So what we are proposing is that she has your room, Lucio, and you can share with us. It'll be lovely – the three of us all snuggled up together!'

The thought of it actually made me want to chuck up, but the Count seemed quite taken with the idea. I was soon rearranging things in his bedroom and managed to produce a steaming poo in the corner in no time at all to personalise my new territory.

Proud though I was of my poo, I was pretty appalled at the lack of room service and made sure that the EM realised she was falling short when she eventually stirred herself. I shot past her and into the lounge where the dollops were sprawled over every available surface. Boy – did that wake their livers up!

Eventually it was decided that I should have the freedom of the bedrooms and only retire to my own room at night. This meant that I had access to the computers in the cupboard they grandly referred to as "the study" and, although I was careful to disguise my delight in the early stages, I realised that world domination was now within my grasp.

I couldn't believe my luck one morning when the EM flung open my bedroom door with a cheery greeting – I think she may have said, 'For Heaven's sake you've done another poo in the corner!' but I knew she actually meant that she loved me very much and couldn't imagine life without me. Anyway, out I popped and as she disappeared, closing the door into the dining room behind her, I bounded out into the inner hall to see Count Lucio looming out of the computer room! I chirruped encouragingly and jumped on his back. Soon we were careering up and down the hall with me clinging on like a little tabby jockey. I hadn't enjoyed myself so much for ages, but then the great lump started yowling and the EM hurtled into view.

'Poor Lucio!' she shouted, flapping a tea towel at me, 'stop it this minute, Tiny! You're frightening the poor boy!'

With that she grabbed me and hauled me off his back, then picked Lucio up and kissed him. If he'd been frightened before, he was absolutely terrified then and proceeded to scrape at his face in a futile attempt to remove the EM's rather startling crimson lipstick from his gleaming fur.

Fun though it had been to frighten the Italian stallion, it made me realise that there was no prospect of the great black lump playing a significant role in my world domination project. Benjamin Wobble would also have to be discounted; not only was he more wobbly than the EM after a bottle of El Plonko, but he was inclined to have what the EM and Poor Roger quaintly referred to as "funny turns" if anybody so much as looked at him without making an appointment. As the EM was fond of saying, 'Little Benjy isn't like other cats; he's a *very* special boy.'

Unfortunately, he would have had to go some to distinguish himself at Tresta Towers, where problems and funny turns were as plentiful as the lumps in the EM's custard. In their different ways, each resident was "special" if being pathetic and needy counted for anything. I too was "special", but in a sparkling, celebrity kind of way and it was only a matter of time before the world would be forced to acknowledge my unique talents. Meanwhile, I would practice on the EM, Poor Roger and the feline misfits at Tresta Towers.

At least my efforts to socialise with Count Lucio and the ginger bagpipes had produced a reaction, but I might as well have been invisible as far as two of the residents were concerned. When I shot towards the moth-eaten old tabby known as Bonnie Bun-Bun, she gazed into the middle distance before drifting vaguely towards the running buffet of Kitty-dins and walking through it. I tried to engage her attention, but realised I was on a loser when she barged into me, almost rendering me unconscious with a powerful gust of pilchard-laden breath.

Just as alarming was my first encounter with St Petersburg Cloud Princess. At first, I assumed the creature hadn't got eyes because its head resembled a fuzzy tennis ball with no distinguishing features. It was only when she sneezed a dreadful snot-laden jet of air in my direction that I observed a small opening filled with tiny shark-like teeth, which presumably was meant to be a mouth. Some way behind this was a tiny button, which I could only assume was her nose and eventually I made out two enormous eyes peering at the world from behind a trellis of tousled fur.

I was trying to attract this creature's attention when the EM rushed in clutching a fistful of cottonwool and began wiping her face with more enthusiasm than skill. A series of guinea-pig squeaks issued forth by way of protest and the EM was forced to abandon the project when the victim sneezed over her varifocals.

'Bella!' she shrieked, 'you really are a messy little monster! You've sneezed all over Mummy's glasses!'

Within seconds, the EM was consumed with guilt at having hurt her feelings.

'Mummy's very sorry, Bella! How could she have been so spiteful! Poor little girl – Mummy loves her special Persian very much!'

Bella glared balefully at the silly woman for a moment or two before disappearing into the depths of her igloo bed on the dining table. I felt a grudging admiration for the creature's ability to manipulate the EM, but it was hard to imagine her finding her way out of that igloo, let alone playing a major role in my masterplan.

CHAPTER THREE

The Dream and The Reality

In no time at all the EM had decided that "Tiny" was too small a name for a cat of my wide-ranging talents and glamorous good looks and decided that I should be "hyphenated". I was alarmed when I heard her talking about this; I thought I'd already had the operation and I certainly didn't want a repeat performance. It soon became clear, however, that this would be an entirely painless procedure: I would henceforth be known as "Miss Tiny Trixie-Tribble" – a name that would stand me in good stead when I attended international conferences or was interviewed by that lumpy old Jeremy Paxman.

It hadn't taken me long to realise that the felines weren't the only challenged creatures at Tresta Towers. The people at the vets' surgery in Sidcup had been quite disturbingly bright, whereas the EM and Poor Roger often struggled to identify what day it was without a desperate rummage through diaries and the jungle of post-it notes on the fridge door.

The morning routine was a protracted affair, involving a considerable amount of dirt-tray clearance, not to mention encouragement and lavish praise. Benjamin Wobble would fling his flabby ginger body into a tray the size of a swimming pool and whirl around so that the floor was liberally coated in bone-crunching gravel. A series of grunts would in due course indicate that he'd got down to business.

'Well done, Benjy-Boo!' the EM would trill ecstatically, 'you are just *soooooo* clever! Now hang on, you haven't quite finished…there's one more bit to come. Too late! Bugger.'

A shimmering amber lake would indicate that St Petersburg Cloud Princess had descended from the dining table to perform on the floor, while a flurry of puppy pads confirmed that once again it had been a wet night for the ancient Bonnie Bun-Bun.

The marginally less challenged would be desperate to fling themselves into the garden, preferring the relative peace of the damp borders to the EM's shrill and entirely superfluous commentary on their toileting activities.

One of my favourite morning projects was breaking through the barricades into the dining room to rough up the dollops while the EM lurched through with a cup of tea. This resulted in much spillage and some appalling language. The whole performance would be repeated later in the day only this time it would inevitably involve El Plonko instead of tea. Occasionally, the red stuff would splash over my immaculate tabby fur – horrible!

I was very busy during the day brushing up on my computer skills. At first, Poor Roger was fascinated by my antics and would bore people rigid with lively accounts of me patting the screen with my paw as the cursor jumped around, but this amusement diminished rapidly as he realised that I had attained a level of proficiency which he could only dream about.

Things reached a tricky stage one day when he was engaged on his family tree research and I was sitting at his elbow, bored out of my pretty little head and waiting for him to wander off so that I could crack on with my world domination spreadsheets. By the time he'd found some boring old relative in 1752, I'd just about had enough and leapt on the keyboard with all four paws.

'Dead!' he shrieked, pushing me off the desk. 'That's it – completely dead!'

The door flew open and in blundered the EM. 'Whatever's happened?' she cried, 'where is she? What do you mean – she can't be dead!'

I'd been lurking in the bathroom and nipped out to weave between the EM's chunky legs. The poor woman looked as if she'd seen a ghost and scooped me up.

'Tiny! Are you okay? What were you talking about, Roger? Why did you think she was dead?'

'Not the cat! The computer. She's killed it. I'd just reached a really interesting stage in my research and was on the brink of tracing the great grandparents of my great-great-great-aunt sixteen times removed and she stood on the keyboard. There was a sad sort of groaning squeak from the computer and the screen went blank.'

'Is that all?' snapped the EM, 'I thought you meant something dreadful had happened to poor little Tiny!'

I suppose I'm particularly sensitive, but I detected a slight frostiness between the happy couple for some hours following this brisk exchange of views. After a mere two hours, the computer screen flickered back to life, but Poor Roger's fascinating if somewhat distant relative had fallen prey to the cyberspace gremlins and was never seen again.

There was a further spat later in the day when they were getting ready for a sophisticated evening at the

Ferret and Trouserleg – a local hostelry famed for its chunky chips and exclusive wines from little-known vineyards to the east of Vladivostock.

Seeing Poor Roger rummaging fruitlessly in the stationery cupboard, the EM's curiosity eventually got the better of her. 'What exactly are you looking for?' she asked in a clipped manner.

'My trousers! Have you seen them? You washed them the other day – I saw them on the line.'

I detected a hint of blame in this response and it seemed I was not alone.

'Have you looked in the wardrobe? I know it was a silly thing to do, but I decided to hang them up in there rather than put them in the deep freeze or the microwave.'

By the time they returned, all was sweetness and light. That is to say, the EM had done full justice to the El Plonko and Poor Roger had stuffed himself to the hilt with forbidden pies and chips.

For a while I had treasured some hope that a certain black cat, rejoicing in the unlikely name of Stumpy Malone, might join me in my quest for world domination – in a junior post, of course. With my keen observation skills, it didn't take me long to realise he lacked hind paws, but I thought I detected a certain brightness in the eyes which was conspicuously absent elsewhere.

My hopes were cruelly dashed one evening when I saw a cat igloo moving erratically towards me and realised that Stumpy Malone was inside it. When I challenged him about this apparent silliness, he smirked and said he was practicing being a spy.

'So you think the enemy won't notice a large, fur-encrusted igloo moving across the carpet, do you?' I sneered.

'Well, nobody else noticed me here!' he said, failing totally to comprehend the unique nature of the arrangements at Tresta Towers. There are few places in my experience where a snotty-nosed Persian cat resides in an even snottier igloo on the dining table and even quite sensible visitors accept this as normal.

"The Girls" – a misnomer if ever there was one – were a pair of female cats rattling around in that wide and infinitely flexible age group loosely termed 'middle age'. One of them – Miss Elizabeth – had a thin-lipped, sneering sort of smile that could have indicated intelligence, but was far more likely to signify spitefulness and self-interest, if the smack in the face I received from that skinny white paw was anything to go by. Apparently, she had been born with paralysed back legs and was brought into the EM's inexpert care as a four week old kitten. Weeks of intensive physiotherapy had succeeded in getting Lizzie on her feet and the EM still refers to her as her "Miracle Kitten", which is enough to make anyone either chuck up on the spot or strangle both of them.

Miss Isabelle, a rather faded little black and white number, suffered from memory problems and lacked co-ordination, resulting in some unfortunate tumbles when she stepped backwards into space from lofty scratching towers. I soon realised that Miss Isabelle lived in a world full of excitement because she was incapable of remembering anything for more than five minutes. When she was a kitten there were dark mutterings about "water on the brain", resulting in some very bad jokes about "taps on the head". Anyway, the old bitch was 15 years old by the time I met her, having survived more serious illnesses than PetPlan could throw a claim form at.

I have to confess to feeling a grudging admiration for Evie – a perfectly dreadful black girl who had carried rudeness to an art form. She screamed to be let in, screamed to be let out and trashed every plate of food she was offered, dragging coats, handbags and other cats across the floor in an attempt to bury the offending dish. She also stayed out at night, causing untold wailing and gnashing of teeth, not to mention tensions between her doting humans.

I'd been at Tresta Towers for a couple of months before I realised there were three other felines who had the sense to live outside and express their utter contempt for everybody and everything as frequently as possible. Delilah, a fluffy tortoiseshell, Spitfire, a rusty black, and Pansy, a small piebald number, were referred to by the EM and Poor Roger as "our beautiful wild girls". Before anybody works themselves into a state about these poor cats, I should perhaps make it clear that they received a minimum of three meals a day and had more houses than the Queen.

I resolved to make their acquaintance at the earliest opportunity.

CHAPTER FOUR

My New Career

Just as I was getting the EM and Poor Roger trained, they dodged off for a few days leaving us in the care of a woman universally loved and revered – by Benjamin Wobble anyway. Auntie K, as the woman is known, bounced in with a cheery smile and left after two days, looking as if she'd been through a tsunami followed by a clout round the head from a meteorite.

I'm not saying I was difficult, but if they thought they could go off and leave me like that without some fairly drastic repercussions, they were in for a shock. As for that Auntie K person coming in here, telling me I couldn't have access to *my* computer! The nerve of the woman!

I lulled Auntie K into thinking I was really quite a sweet little thing, then did an enormous poo on the bed. Serve her right! The beauty of it was that she didn't discover it until bedtime, then had to strip all the covers off – dear me, what a fuss! Even though I couldn't hear properly, I could sense her pain and screamed my sympathy until she flung open the door in a right old state.

'If this is your idea of a joke, Miss TinyTrixie-Tribble, it certainly isn't mine!' she burbled. 'I shall tell the EM and Poor Roger about your behaviour – don't think I won't!'

I smirked at her, secure in the knowledge that they

would be absurdly flattered by the thought that I'd missed them so much – or that my bowels had.

As soon as old Melon-Chops arrived back, I flung myself at her, chirruping away and rubbing my face against any part of her anatomy within reach. Predictably, she was enchanted.

'Mummy's here, Sweetheart! Everything's okay now. You are a silly girl to be so upset! Did you think we weren't coming back?'

I managed a simpering and grateful look which took a bit of doing, but it was worth it. In that moment I realised that world domination was but a few poos away.

Inevitably, there was a price to pay in that I had to listen to them droning on about all the exciting things they'd done on their "holiday". They kept on about the Spitfire Museum and at first I thought it was something to do with Spitfire the feral cat. My interest plummeted when I realised they were talking about some boring old aeroplane. Just as dull was the side-splitting tale about Poor Roger thinking the EM was playing footsie with him in the pub, only to find it was a Jack Russell Terrier that had taken a fancy to his walking boots.

Although life jogged along pleasantly enough, a cat of my intelligence and versatility needed a fresh challenge to achieve her full potential. I also realised that it would be an act of extreme selfishness not to bring enlightenment to the poor ignorant dollops that abound in the largely uncharted jungle that is Surrey. It was in this spirit of charity that I agreed to accompany the EM and Poor Roger when they mentioned giving a talk on cat care to a group of pensioners.

There was much anguishing about which collar I should wear. Would the pink sparkly number be seen as too girlie and frivolous? Would black velvet be just a tad too understated? In the end, we settled for dark blue with a suggestion of glitter – glamorous, but with just the right hint of gravitas.

Luckily it didn't take the humans long to get ready, because by the time all my luggage had been loaded up we had to get a bit of a shift on. I sat in my portable cage surveying the hall as the dear old souls tottered in, chirruping in a welcoming manner and trying to reassure them that the EM was fairly harmless – even though that spiky hair and glinting varifocals did give her the look of a deranged and short-sighted orang-utan.

Once everybody had settled down, I was released from my cage and made it my business to bound around introducing myself to everyone. Poor Roger had brought my laser light toy and I rushed around chasing it to rapturous applause. I can't remember when I'd enjoyed myself so much – unless it was the time that the EM and Poor Roger were lying in bed worrying about not being able to see the butterfly lights draped so tastefully around the water feature.

'I'm going to take those lights straight back to the garden centre!' exclaimed Poor Roger, shuddering with indignation. 'It's been sunny all day today so they should be twinkling away like anything!'

About an hour later the EM remembered she'd left the washing on the line so that the merrily twinkling lights were totally obscured by Bonnie Bun-Bun's bedding.

I digress. One of the best things about the afternoon with the pensioners was the fact that I completely upstaged the EM, who constantly struggled to interest the audience in the fascinating world of flea treatments and microchipping, while I jumped on laps and rubbed against faces. It goes without saying that they were besotted with me and it really wouldn't have mattered if the EM had been there or not.

On the way home Poor Roger remarked that I would no doubt be exhausted and likely to take to my bed for hours. Wrong! I erupted out of that cat carrier like the proverbial Champagne cork and bounded around for ages. Even when I did fall asleep, I was busy dreaming of glories to come. I thought I might even use that sweet little village hall for rallying the faithful to my cause – before moving on to the Albert Hall or possibly the O2 arena, of course.

Predictably, the EM took all the credit for my successful debut and I had to listen to her boring people rigid about her talent-spotting skills. If she was so clever at identifying talent, why on earth was Tresta Towers overflowing with cats who were almost all wobbly, senile or downright bonkers?

Before long the EM was busily planning our future engagements – this time she was mercilessly targeting the younger captive audiences to be found in schools and Beaver and Brownie groups. She assumed that she enjoyed my unquestioning support for these projects, which was a bit of a cheek, but it didn't take me long to realise that this was exactly the opportunity I needed. Access to those malleable young minds would be just the thing if I was to achieve world leader status and so I purred ingratiatingly when the EM shoved yet another entry in my diary.

I even helped with the stuffing of the goody bags

which we took with us on our educational talks. These bags were meant to contain pens and leaflets – all guaranteed to make the children's hearts beat faster and fill them with unbounded gratitude. Some lucky children would also receive lumps of fur and – when St Petersburg Cloud Princess generously assisted – the odd lump of Persian snot, no doubt ensuring that they would become lifelong supporters of Dogs Trust at an early age.

I resolved to extract as many new collars as possible over the coming months; after all, nobody expects that Tess Daly person to turn up on *Strictly Come Dancing* wearing the same old frock week after week.

Meanwhile it had come to my notice that some cats were being fed yummier food than others. St Petersburg Cloud Princess, the raggedy old Persian number, was munching her way through shedloads of very expensive food, specially designed for cats with faces like dinner plates who couldn't manage to wedge normal shaped biscuits into their sadly inadequate mouths. Other members of the gang had also managed to convince the EM that they had difficulty eating ordinary food for a whole host of suspect reasons.

Whizzy was apparently totally incapable of eating normal food because she only had three legs and Evie absolutely had to have the special Persian stuff because she would leave home unless she was fed with it every hour, on the hour. Delilah and Spitfire, who rejoiced in their wildness, liked nothing better than to sneak through the patio doors and cram as much of this food into their cavernous mouths as possible before the EM caught them in the act. It was like a feline version of a time-limited trolley dash, only much more dangerous if you happened to get between the wild girls and their food.

Coincidentally, it wasn't long before I was wolfing down the special stuff as fast as I could go because the ordinary food started to cause an irritating dryness in my throat and I became a martyr to projectile vomiting.

Having secured this small, but vital, victory I found I was able to tolerate the other cats with a degree of equanimity. My sunny disposition took a knock, however, when I contemplated those pointy-nosed badgers. They turned up every night to vacuum up a veritable banquet of goodies and trashed the garden as a token of their gratitude. In spite of this rudeness the EM and Poor Roger doted on the wretched things and even served coq au vin one night as a result of over-provisioning on the part of a deluded friend. The badgers became disturbingly merry on this occasion and struggled to find their way home – a scenario all-too familiar to the EM and her friends on their "girls'" nights out.

I didn't mind about Poor Roger feeding the birds, however, because he was obviously just trying to provide us with a bit of audio-visual entertainment. He would spend hours wobbling about on a step-ladder, stuffing boring things like peanuts into a plastic tube, only to see it trashed by the squirrels as soon as he'd turned his back.

The birds were quite amusing too – particularly those rude pigeons who for some reason thought the feeding platform was the avian equivalent of a cheap hotel room. Often they would get in a right old flap and end up plummeting into the badgers' leftovers – hardly the last word in romantic encounters.

CHAPTER FIVE

The Pen Is Mightier Than The Sword

One day, when idly flicking through Poor Roger's emails, I came across a diagram of what appeared to be a house for very small people. For some time I'd been thinking that things were getting a bit cramped in what passes for a "study" and wondered who would be moving into the new accommodation – the EM or Poor Roger?

The dimensions of the house were decidedly snug, but I thought they would probably be happy enough. There was even a sweet little shelf where the EM could keep her El Plonko and the various potions required for those "bad hair" days, when the tortoiseshell tufts resisted every attempt to subdue their spiky scariness.

My mood changed abruptly when I saw Poor Roger's reply headed, "Tiny's House". The deceitfulness of it all! When I thought how I'd sat on their laps and shared their suppers! Proof, if proof were needed, of the duplicity of the human race and of dumpy pensioners in particular. I felt an overwhelming sense of relief that I had kept my plans for world domination to myself and tried to feel grateful that I had discovered their treachery at this early stage.

The EM had by now decided that my wardrobe was inadequate for a star in the making and we settled down to browse various Google websites purporting to make must-have accessories for discerning "kitten-kats". I was just warming to the idea of a rather skimpy leopard skin outfit when the EM assumed her "Disgusted of Tonbridge Wells" expression and clicked the "close" tab before I'd decided whether to have the pink background or the lime green.

'For Heaven's sake!' she muttered, 'I thought they were advertising cat harnesses! How can anybody wear underwear like that? It must cut in dreadfully! And it certainly doesn't look as if they have cotton gussets...'

So that was the end of that. Instead of some slinky little number, I ended up with a harness in a trendy camouflage pattern, which I supposed would be more suitable for bounding around village halls and showing those vulnerable kids who was boss.

The training sessions I organised for the EM were quite demanding as she was such a slow learner. She fitted the harness on me without too much trouble, but was very slow to grasp that once the lead was attached, she was supposed to follow wherever I wanted to go.

In the end she more or less got the message. I think the point was made by running round and round her legs until she looked like a trussed chicken in baggy jeans, before I fell to the floor spluttering. I'm still not sure why this worked so effectively – the lead was attached to the harness which went round my dear little tabby body, not my throat. Mind you, if there's anyone around who actually believes that humans are at the top of the evolutionary ladder, they're probably still trying to open tins with a toothbrush.

I had a lovely time taking the EM for walks in the garden and I really think it did her good to get a bit of exercise in the fresh air. She was slow to see the fun of running through the undergrowth in the "conservation area" of the garden and made a terrible fuss when a bramble lacerated her knuckles, but generally the experiment was a huge success. The wild girls sat on the fence with superior expressions on their pinched little faces, but even they were forced to admire my technique when I smacked the EM into the beech tree with a sudden change of direction.

Once she'd mastered walking with the harness, I thought she should progress to a more sophisticated level of interactive play. Up to now, she'd achieved an adequate level of competence with the laser light toy, until I made it quite clear that shining the light in a straight line was pretty damn boring. A succession of jaw-wrenching yawns forced her to be more inventive and within a comparatively short time – I think it was about three weeks – she had progressed to a light-wiggling technique which included the light climbing up walls and disappearing behind doors. I would reward particularly inventive manoeuvres with a succession of chirrups and punish laziness by pointedly turning my back on her and washing my bottom.

The EM had also achieved a reasonable level of proficiency with the goldfish hanging from a fishing rod, although I worried slightly that she seemed to think it was real.

'Poor goldfish!' she would exclaim as I kicked seven bells out it, 'Freddie Fish didn't deserve that, did he?'

Jerking the thing around seemed to give her enormous pleasure and she would be quite tired after ten minutes or so of intensive play, settling down with her book and giving us all a much-needed break.

Soon I began to feel she might be ready for another challenge, so once again we settled down to Google "interactive toys". We'd got as far as the ones that required three AAA batteries when the EM's face took on a strange mottled quality.

'Well! Whatever are you supposed to do with that?' she squeaked, 'whatever it is, we're not getting one!'

We finally settled on a mat thing that was supposed to have a mouse running about under it. I thought at the time this would be a bit more than the EM was likely to cope with and could see the El Plonko bill increasing dramatically as a result. When it arrived, she struggled to get the bloody thing out of the box and it was painfully evident that the sophisticated techniques required to actually play the game would always elude her. To say I wore myself out trying to show her what to do is an understatement. I would fling myself at the "mouse" as it randomly moved under the mat, only to find that the EM had wandered off to ring one of her mad friends.

In the end, I ripped the thing to pieces and stuffed the bits under the bed. Pulling them out with great clumps of dust and fur attached was much more entertaining and I always made sure I did it when visitors came. The clumps actually looked remarkably like mice and a glimpse of them wafting across the bathroom floor had many a desperate woman emerging in haste with her skirt hitched up in her knickers.

While we were waiting for my little house to arrive, the EM and Poor Roger became dangerously excited about the publication of Stumpy Malone's book, *Paws for Thought*. That black witch, Evie, had written one the year before – as if anybody cared what she thought or did –

and Stumpy had followed in her rather elegant black pawsteps. As the EM was fond of saying, it was just as well that he had front paws or he wouldn't have been able to type. How subtle is that!

As a result of this feverish activity, the EM found herself posting books out to all the people who were too terrified to say they didn't want to buy the wretched volume. One day in the local post office – an establishment not noted for its sparkling repartee – she found herself at the counter with a parcel addressed to Miss Toffee Pop, this being the sweet-natured dog in Southampton who had struck up a lively email correspondence with the challenged ginger lump, Benjamin Wobble.

'Miss Toffee Pop is a dog,' trilled the EM, by way of explanation as the girl gazed at the label blankly.

The counter clerk's expression – if indeed she had one – didn't change.

'You never know with these foreign names,' she said. 'I didn't think much about it.'

In the run-up to the arrival of the contentious "Tiny House", the EM and Poor Roger decided that the back garden should be knocked into shape. Quite why they felt this to be necessary remains a mystery as the house was to be erected on the patio with extensive views of the grassy patch so lovingly excavated by the worm-raking badgers. However, we are talking about humans for whom logic was one of life's optional extras, along with sensible shoes and vitamin pills, and they generally shuffled along from day to day without any logical thoughts conspicuously interfering with their activities.

On this occasion, they rushed out in to the garden minutes before darkness fell with a resounding thud and proceeded to rip out armfuls of weeds. They also made a spirited attack on the catmint bush, which had had to be coaxed along under an inverted hanging basket in its youth, but which was now threatening to invade the bungalow and eat us all.

Predictably, when they staggered indoors, the smell of catnip was overpowering and although as a sophisticated feline I can take or leave the stuff, to Benjamin Wobble and his more challenged companions, the EM's baggy sweatshirt was absolutely irresistible.

'Benjy Boo has missed Mummy so much!' cooed the EM as the ginger flounder flopped all over her, dribbling copiously. 'Mummy wasn't out for long, Darling – you could see Mummy and Daddy, couldn't you? There was no need to worry!'

No sooner had Benjy subsided into a drug-induced coma than Bonnie Bun-Bun caught a whiff of Poor Roger's jeans and slid down his legs to land like an unoccupied nightdress case on the mat.

I began to think that there could be some merit in acquiring a second property, if only to escape for a few hours from the madness that was Tresta Towers and resolved to show interest in the "Tiny House" when it arrived. As Poor Roger gazed excitedly at the drawings, I sat on his lap and nodded sagely when he pointed to its state of the art features, stifling a yawn as he "finger-walked" me through the door for the umpteenth time.

When the great day finally dawned, I was pretty well worn out with the whole thing, but managed to summon the strength to leer menacingly at the men erecting it as I reclined on the bedroom windowsill. I had perfected this technique with the window cleaner – an inoffensive young man – by leaping at each window as he appeared. Of course, it would have been a lot more fun if he'd been on a ladder, but as Tresta Towers is a dumpy little bungalow I was denied the rewarding spectacle of him plummeting from a great height. He still looked pretty shaken, however, and remained convinced that there were several small and incredibly beautiful young tabbies in residence when, of course, it was just little old me flying around with my usual exquisite grace. I did catch my toe on some hideous ornament, but decided not to sue for damages on this occasion.

CHAPTER SIX

Stepping Stones To Success

Having my own establishment gave me the opportunity to further my acquaintance with the feral cats and the various wild animals that trundled and flitted through the garden as if they owned the place. Delilah and Spitfire had lived here for years and managed to secure everything they wanted without giving an inch and I felt I might learn something to my advantage by getting on friendlier terms.

Although the EM was fond of telling people how silly Delilah was, I began to see that there was more going on in that vacant-looking tortoiseshell head than the EM was giving her credit for. She would only have to appear at the patio door for Poor Roger to rush out with yet another plate of Kittydins and he was always worrying that the sleeping bag in her cat cabin might not be thick enough to keep the old baggage warm. Sometimes, Delilah would arch her back and allow the humans to stroke her then, just as they were congratulating themselves on at last making headway with her after twelve years, she would look at them as if they had horns and disappear for hours.

Nobody was ever likely to stroke old "Smiler" Spitfire and retain all their digits. She had arrived as a small black ball of hatred and after thirteen years she had evolved into a much larger, rather rusty ball of hatred – an object lesson to all those sycophantic cats who think they'll never get another morsel if they so much as spit in their owner's eye.

The third feral, Pansy, rarely entered the back garden – preferring instead to prance about out the front and frighten motorists to death by flinging herself across the road at the last moment. I decided not to bother with her and to concentrate on the more promising material to be found in the back garden.

The first few times that the EM put me into my new house were characterised by frequent visits to ascertain if I was falling to bits without her inane chatter to sustain me. This really got on my nerves, so I retired to my sleeping quarters and had a really good sulk. Needless to say, the EM totally misinterpreted my actions and reported to Poor Roger that I seemed very tired after all the excitement, but at least she left me alone for a while to do some girlie bonding with my new friends – after I'd shredded the net curtains so thoughtfully provided by one of the EM's cronies.

It wasn't long before Spitfire appeared, closely followed by Delilah. I knew that it was important to start as I meant to go on, so I spat at them and growled menacingly.

'Whatever was that funny noise?' mewed Spitfire, 'was it your stomach rumbling, Delilah? I told you not to eat that mouse we found under the wheelie bin...'

With that, they frolicked off into the woods without a backward glance. Bitch-cats! Just wait till I'm holding my first rally at The Albert Hall! We'll see who feels like making catty remarks then! I was hopeful that the rather glamorous dog fox I'd watched from the window would make a more satisfactory second-in-command, but any hopes of seeing him were dashed by the untimely appearance of the EM.

'Poor little girl!' she trilled, 'did you think Mummy had forgotten you? Of course she wouldn't do such a thing! Naughty Daddy for keeping Mummy chatting when she should have been looking after Tiny Trixie-Tribble! Let's get you indoors before Mr Fox comes along and frightens you!'

And I only saw the bulky old badgers from the bedroom window because the EM was convinced that I'd hate to be left in my house once it got dark. This proved beyond all reasonable doubt that the woman inhabits some parallel universe where cats sleep all night and potter about happily during daylight hours. Hello!! Cats are nocturnal – and have been since the first perfectly formed feline placed its dainty little killer paws on the planet. Perhaps I've missed something and there's been some evolutionary twist; perhaps fish are trotting across the Sahara as I write and tigers are tucking into hearty salads while they worry about the wellbeing of helpless baby antelopes – but possibly not.

It was a source of considerable frustration to me that I couldn't communicate with the badgers, Moonbeam and Brillo, because of their well-established underground connections. A cat without my steely resolve could so easily have despaired of realising her dream of world domination, surrounded as I was by dribbling, dementia and a tidal wave of incontinence. Some of the cats were in a bit of a state as well.

I had hoped to make some headway with Miss Elizabeth, who alone amongst the Special Needs Unit appeared to have some vestige of a brain. With this in mind, I lurked in the study late one evening knowing that the humans were sprawled out on the sofa eagerly devouring *Murder on the Orient Express*, featuring Peter Ustinov at the turn of the previous century, and pounced on Miss Elizabeth as she wiggled unsuspectingly into view.

Unfortunately, she showed no inclination to enter into meaningful discussion about how she might assist me in my quest, choosing instead to clock me one and spit in my face. I drew myself up to my full ten inches and shoved her into the box I keep for such eventualities. My mind raced as I wondered how much I could extract by way of ransom for the miserable old bag, but before I could complete my calculations, Miss Elizabeth started to scream.

There was a confused yell from the sofa and then the EM's voice rose shrilly into the stratosphere.

'Roger – do something! It's Lucio – he must have cornered poor little Stumpy!'

She then continued, without drawing breath, in a much softer tone. 'Don't worry, Darling! Daddy's going to tell Lucio off! Mr Bully doesn't live here, does he?'

If Lucio was slightly surprised, relaxing as he was on the other sofa, this sort of thing obviously happened so often that it wasn't worth raising so much as a giant black paw in protest.

'He's on the sofa!' countered Poor Roger, after a head-banging scramble under the dining table. 'The poor bloody cat's on the sofa – the noise is coming from the study. We'd better get in there quickly!'

By now, predictably, Miss Elizabeth was milking the situation for all she was worth and gasping in an exaggerated fashion.

'Oh my God! She's having a heart attack!' shrieked the

EM. 'Poor, sweet girl! Tiny Trixie-Tribble – you've gone too far this time!'

With that, Miss Elizabeth was extracted from the box – where she was really enjoying herself – and clasped to the EM's takeaway-splattered jumper. I vaguely remember the EM lecturing me about bad behaviour, but there was a spider on the bathroom ceiling and my attention had wandered.

'We've nursed a viper to our bosoms!' declared the EM. 'You can take the cat out of Sidcup, but you can't take Sidcup out of the cat.'

What Sidcup had ever done to the EM to merit this sniping, I can't imagine, but I just shrugged my little tabby shoulders and gave my flying bat toy a swipe.

It all came down to petty jealousy with the EM. A few days previously, my lovely Uncle Steven had presented me with a very luxurious scratching tower and the EM would have given a great deal to be able to perch on the padded seat that afforded such wonderful views of the garden. She would watch me scampering up and down and pretend to be worried that I would fall and hurt myself, but deep down she was picturing herself on the top level, casually swinging her dumpy little legs while Benjy and the other dollops looked on admiringly.

Sometimes, the EM and Poor Roger would delude themselves into thinking that they were coping well enough with the challenges of life at Tresta Towers to offer their services elsewhere. In reality, of course, they lurched from one crisis to another and spent most of their time trying to remember who they were.

'I'm just popping up to Karen's to do some feral kitten-handling!' trilled the EM one morning. 'I don't know what time I'll be back – it depends whether I have to go to the Walk-In Clinic.'

'Why would you have to go there?' enquired Poor Roger, occupied as he was with extracting my toy bat from under the bed.

'It's just if I get bitten, of course!' snapped the EM. 'They're wild babies and if they get frightened they might bite.'

Well, if those kittens weren't frightened by a mad woman wearing a jumper with a dinosaur on it, they wouldn't be frightened of anything. I began to wonder if I could get my paws on them as they sounded just what I needed to help me achieve world domination.

A few hours later she returned and appeared to be relatively unscathed, if you discounted a few pulled threads here and there – particularly on her face.

'They were such poppets,' exclaimed the EM. 'You would have loved them, Trixie-Tribble! After a bit of spitting, they were all quite happy to be held and some of them even purred.'

What a letdown! Those kittens should be ashamed of themselves.

Speaking of letdowns, I felt a minute surge of hope when I saw the EM and Poor Roger dragging St Petersburg Cloud Princess out of her igloo because the old tart actually made quite a fight of it. Could I have misjudged her? Was there a revolutionary spirit lurking under that mucky candyfloss?

'Dear Bella's being very tricky,' gasped the EM as she grappled with one fuzzy extremity after the other. 'You'll have to hang on tight while I shave these lumps off her bottom...'

38

Bella

Ben and Friend

Bun-Bun

Delilah

Elizabeth

Evie

Isabelle

Lucio

Pheasant

Pigeon

Spitfire

Stumpy and Ben

Stumpy

Tiny Trixie-Tribble

Tiny

Whizzy

I was counting the seconds until the old Persian severed their arteries with one slash of a razor sharp claw! I would embrace her warmly and welcome her to the sisterhood; I would still be in charge, of course, but she could be a spy and keep me informed about dastardly plots, such as a plan to purchase cheaper cat food or have all my claws clipped. I've seen what they did to Stumpy Malone! I don't believe for a minute he was born without hind paws.

Seconds later, St Petersburg Cloud Princess was rolling all over the dining table, purring her stupid fuzzy head off and the EM was in a state of ecstasy.

'I never believed we'd be able to do it,' she gabbled. 'Look at that huge lump of poo I've shaved off! Look – it's on the table, by the vinegar bottle.'

CHAPTER SEVEN

Learning From History

While I was out in my increasingly luxurious Tiny House (the EM and Poor Roger were forever introducing fleecy little blankets and heart-shaped cushions) my musings took on a more philosophical bent and I found myself reflecting on the achievements of my ancestors. Not for these cats the subservient, slipper-fetching antics of those sycophantic canine dollops! What's with all that suicidal insistence on laying down their lives to protect their human, when any animal with an ounce of commonsense would clear off in the opposite direction?

I briefly toyed with the idea of recruiting a couple of dogs to assist me in my campaign for world domination but ruled it out because there isn't a mutt on this planet that can keep a secret for more than two seconds. Take, for example, Toffee Pop – the sweet dog who has unwisely entered into a prolific email correspondence with the lascivious Benjamin Wobble. This innocent creature has imparted all sorts of information about her household, including details about El Plonko consumption and sausage suppers. Cats, on the other paw, are more than capable of keeping their own counsel.

Felines are able to keep secrets because we don't really care much about anything except food, warmth and the occasional catnip fix. During the Cold War, for example, you could hardly put your foot down in Red Square without tripping over a Russian Blue who might really have been a British Blue, depending on whether caviar or kippers were on the menu.

A fine example of human reliance on the superior qualities of cats was the sorry state that Ramses got into in Ancient Egypt. It took him a while to catch on, of course, and meanwhile the mice were holding some pretty mean parties on the grain sacks, dancing and singing *Grain Drops Are Falling on My Head* until poor old Ramses thought he'd go mad.

One evening, having nipped into the granary for a quick smoke, Ramses was amazed to see a line of dead rodents laid out on the ground. A strange purring noise caused him to look up and he saw a beautiful tabby cat nonchalantly washing her whiskers.

'You are my goddess! I shall call you "Mau",' whispered Ramses reverently. 'You have saved my granaries and I shall be forever in your debt!'

Mau smirked. She would much rather have been called "Bubbles" or "Poppy", but that didn't need to be a sticking point. She realised instantly that this was "bum-in-butter" time for her and her family; she'd soon have her relatives installed and a bit of fun round the back of the pyramids with that rather attractive bat-eared tomcat without having to worry about claiming benefits for the next litter of screaming brats.

Fast forward a few years and Ramses began to notice that the cats were now more numerous than the mice had been. It was costing him a fortune to feed Mau and her ever-increasing family as there were hardly any mice left for them to eat. There was only one thing for it: he'd have to contact Cats Protection about getting them neutered and microchipped. He wondered if those little chip things would accommodate hieroglyphics...

Anyway, the result of my deliberations was my emergence as a stronger, more focussed leader and I resolved to waste no time in knocking the residents of Tresta Towers into shape. Unfortunately – as is so frequently the way of things in this benighted establishment – circumstances intervened to sabotage my finely-honed plans.

It was a salutary lesson on the importance of timing. I hadn't given much thought to this Christmas business, other than to fight back a strong urge to savage the EM each time she bounded in with yet another glittery kitten card to shove in my face.

'Just look at this, Trixie-Tribble!' she would squeak, possibly realising that I had very little option with the heartwarming greetings a millimetre from my whiskers. 'Everybody wishes our little new girl a very happy time and I wouldn't be a bit surprised if Father Christmas didn't bring you some really exciting presents on the big day!"

Wow. Imagine my excitement – not. As far as I was concerned, Christmas was getting in the way of my plans and the sooner the jolly reindeer jingled back to the North Pole with that fat old man in his red frock, the better. However, just as I had settled my mind to a fortnight of boredom, forces from the great beyond provided some welcome entertainment.

The first bit of excitement cropped up a couple of days before Christmas. It had been a windy night and I suspect I wasn't the only one to regret stealing some sherry trifle the previous evening. In the morning I peered out into the back garden and noticed that the view was quite different from usual. At first I wondered if Tresta Towers had been snatched up and deposited in alien territory, but soon I realised that this was excessively fanciful and I was just looking into next door's garden. The high wooden fence had vanished overnight.

This meant that there was nothing to prevent the Special Needs Unit felines from marching (or limping, or lurching) into next door's manicured borders – the sort of nightmare that our neighbours would take years to recover from. The EM, predictably, was beside herself with worry that dear little Stumpy Malone with – or should I say without – his missing hind paws would be able to access all sorts of new territory and get into untold scrapes, not realising that the dismal wretch had been hauling himself over the fence for months.

Even St Petersburg Cloud Princess, who rarely emerged from her igloo on the dining table, felt the need to totter into next door, followed by the ancient Bonnie Bun-Bun, yodelling her confusion to the skies. Imagine the joy of the next door neighbours when they opened their curtains to behold this motley crew pottering through their winter pansies!

The next challenge was provided by Count Lucio, who began to vomit at the precise moment that the "Closed" sign went up at our vet's surgery on Christmas Eve. At first, the EM responded with bracing speeches.

'Come along, Lucio! Being sick really shouldn't affect your ability to walk. There's no need to lie in the doorway – we've all noticed you've chucked up.'

An hour later he took himself off into the study and

hid under the desk. The EM was up early on Christmas morning and her mood was distinctly lacking in festive cheer. An hour later, the Count was bundled off to the emergency vet, where a fresh-faced young vet was convinced that the EM was suffering from Munchausen's by Proxy until he did blood tests and found that the Count really wasn't well. Unfortunately, they decided to keep the Count in over Christmas to be tortured by child vets, peeved at missing all the festive fun, but sent the EM home – clutching Lucio's disgustingly soiled blanket – to make our innocent little lives a misery.

The rest of the festive season passed in a predictable blur of El Plonko and too much to eat. The EM made a terrible fuss about giving us all a portion of turkey and the rest of the creepy cats dutifully munched their way through the greasy lumps of pallid meat with grunts and squeaks of appreciation. I buried mine in the bedspread.

When Count Lucio returned late on Boxing Day, he was immediately carried through to the bedroom where he languished stylishly for some days. A whole running buffet was provided and refreshed at regular intervals, while Benjamin Wobble and Bonnie Bun-Bun dribbled and squabbled outside the door. For the remainder of the festive season, it was Count Lucio's appetite or lack of it that dictated the mood. Consumption of a few morsels would be the cause of wild rejoicing, while refusal to even lick at a piece of freshly cooked chicken would have the EM fumbling for the number of the local Samaritans branch.

One event brightened all our lives in various ways and this was the accidental imprisoning of Evie, the wild child of the house, in the summerhouse. A highlight of the EM's morning agenda was racing Stumpy Malone to the badger tunnel at the bottom of the garden. Once she'd covered the badger highway over to prevent the Special Needs Unit from wandering into the woods, she would open up the summerhouse to provide shelter for Whizzy, who had had a terrible turn when she saw my own bijou dwelling and had to be consoled with access to this rather unattractive and utilitarian shed.

As she flung open the door, little Evie dashed out, pausing only to fling a look of intense hatred at the EM. When the EM tottered back into the lounge, she was smiling radiantly.

'You shut poor little Evie in the summerhouse, Roger!' she said – unable to resist apportioning blame even in the midst of her new and slightly disturbing happiness. 'And she'd done a big poo on that new lounger cushion. Guess what? There were absolutely no worms in there. Isn't that wonderful?'

Several vulnerable people were rash enough to visit Tresta Towers and provided us with much innocent amusement during the dark days of winter. One crony of the EM's was anxious to see St Petersburg Cloud Princess who was ensconced in her ghastly old igloo on the dining table and had to be coaxed out with tantalising glimpses of "Mr Combey".

'Come on, Bella,' cooed the EM, 'Mr Combey wants to make Bella look beautiful! And Auntie Sandy's come all the way from the Isle of Wight to see you!'

In due course, a small and bedraggled mop-head revealed itself in the shadowy entrance to the igloo to the intense delight of Mr Combey and Auntie Sandy.

'Oh no!' exclaimed a rather agitated Auntie Sandy, 'what's that on her poor little face?'

The EM peered at our flawless princess and giggled, 'That's her tongue! Since her front teeth fell out, her tongue sticks out. What did you think it was?'

I'm sure it's just coincidence, but we haven't seen Auntie Sandy for a while. Something about stormy seas between the Isle of Wight and Portsmouth...

CHAPTER EIGHT

Back To The Clawing Board

One of the downsides to spending quality time in my special residence was the lack of internet access. If I was the sort of cat to bear a grudge, I would have resented the EM sitting at her desk bashing out endless pointless emails while I – with so much to achieve – had to sit on my paws and watch the world limp by.

This meant that I had to make best use of the facilities when I could get my paws on them and I wasted no time in attempting to establish a worldwide network of like-minded felines.

I had high hopes of making headway with some of Benjamin Wobble's internet chums, but they proved something of a disappointment and none more so than Toffee Pop, who I had hoped would be useful as an informant, even if she couldn't be trusted with a management role. I imagined that she would be like a dog with two tails to receive a communication from a cat with my star quality, but by this time all the poor creature could keep dripping on about was how much she loved Benjy Boo. Not only did she love Benjy Blankety Blank Boo, but so did her owner and everybody else in the household, including a youngster called Marmite, who apparently kissed Benjy's photograph every night before retiring to bed. Pausing only to chuck up, I wasted no time in deleting Toffee Pop from my address book.

Another disappointment was HRH Howard, a naughty tortie from Deal who had been thrust on her unfortunate owners by the EM some years previously. This deluded feline claimed to have traced her ancestry back to the Tudor dynasty and I was almost prepared to go along with this until I received a particularly upsetting response intimating that she couldn't possibly correspond with a cat who had been scraped up from the streets of Sidcup.

Which brings me to Ms Pickle. I suppose all great leaders have their work cut out in the early days, but I have more than a suspicion that if Boadicea had had to cope with Ms Pickle's high-handed manner she might well have stayed at home making saucy little frocks from squirrel skins instead of flinging herself round Britain in that rickety old chariot. Ms Pickle – who I suspect had had things rather too much her own way in her luxurious home at Apethorpe Spa – made it absolutely clear that she had no intention of helping me to achieve world domination because it might make her late for lunch.

In spite of these setbacks, I experienced a surge of optimism when I intercepted an email from a cat called Daisy. This rather handsome black and white boy (yes, boy!) was in the habit of emailing the EM to report on the goings-on in his household and certainly knew how to spill the beans about various mouse-catching escapades. His mother was intent on rescuing these hapless rodents and set great store by her humane traps, much to Daisy's amusement. Daisy, however, turned down my offer of a starring role in the world domination campaign on the basis that this might not leave him enough sleeping time. Has he never watched the televised debates at the House of Lords?

A breakthrough came when I made contact with "The Magnificent Seven" in Japan, who were already coping with bears and other quite uppity creatures by growling and grimacing at them from their sunkissed windowsill. Although there was scope for a more paws-on approach, this was a promising start. With countries to the east of Woking pretty well sewn up, I could concentrate my efforts on the rather more lack-lustre residents closer to home.

I was beginning to make headway with Benjamin Wobble, who had decided he wasn't fritted of me after all. As with all heroic enterprises, there were sacrifices to be made and in this case I had to endure being slobbered over and pinned to the ground when he suddenly dropped off to sleep on top of me. The EM would eventually notice and lift him up, but by then I was as flat as an unoccupied glove puppet.

Evie was probably the most promising of the bunch, but she wasted so much time on her stormy relationship with Count Lucio that I despaired of her ever committing herself fully to the cause. In fact, after a lengthy chat when I had thought I had her full attention, she suddenly mumbled something about how handsome Lucio looked silhouetted against the television screen and I felt an irresistible urge to spit in her pretty little black face. At one time Evie had apparently considered taking over the running of Tresta Towers, only to succumb to Lucio's dubious charms and abandon her project in less time than it takes Benjamin to flop down in front of the EM and send her sprawling.

I decided to give Stumpy Malone another chance to join my crusade. Although he lacked hind paws, there was a knowing look in those big eyes that encouraged me to think there could actually be a few brain cells lurking behind them.

I sidled up to him with a view to asking what he intended to do with his life, apart from poking at Whizzy's fat bottom and making her scream.

'I'm going to be a mighty hunter,' he squeaked, turning to swear through the window at a pair of magpies who were helping themselves to the Wild Girls' breakfast. 'That porky old badger had a narrow escape the other night! All that stopped me catching him was being on the wrong side of the patio door.'

'Don't you ever think about the oppression of the feline race?' I asked, but Stumpy's legendary powers of concentration had already deserted him and he was having a wonderful time making Whizzy scream.

Even the most impassioned revolutionary sometimes needs to recharge her batteries, so rather than wear myself out with this lot of no-hopers I spent some immensely enjoyable time out making a list of the crimes committed by the EM and Poor Roger.

High on the list had to be the incarceration policy which they followed with obvious relish. By about 10pm there would be a roll call and heaven help any of us who could not be accounted for. I have to confess experiencing a grudging admiration for Evie and Stumpy Malone, who on many occasions managed to be one cat or several cats, driving the EM completely batty in the process. Sometimes, Stumpy managed to break out and have a wonderful time catching and crunching up moths while the EM gazed at him fondly, convinced that she was in fact looking at Evie, who enjoyed a later curfew time than our footless friend. Moments later, the sight of Evie, stretching sleepily on the sofa would be followed by panicky searches of the garden and impassioned speeches about the treachery and ungratefulness of the feline race.

They were particularly and annoyingly vigilant when it came to keeping me behind closed doors, making much of my slight deafness and lack of fear. These "problems" would apparently lead to me being run over or eaten by a marauding carnivore; and they say I've got brain damage!!

Another major crime related to the limited availability of yummy things. The EM and Poor Roger could, of course, sit stuffing their faces with as much pork crackling and chocolate as they could get their hands on, but had no hesitation in ordering up sacks of low calorie rubbish for us. Benjamin Wobble came as close to being vexed as I have ever seen the ginger dollop when the EM flushed some really tasty food down the loo, "in case it was infected". The source of the infection was alleged to be a virulent germ contracted by Count Lucio, but nothing will convince me that spite was not the sole motivation for this hurtful act.

The complete absence of any meaningful consultation was a perpetual trial. Time and time again, one or more of us would be snatched up by the EM, bundled into a cat carrier and driven off to the vet's surgery where we would be subjected to a variety of indignities without so much as a "by your leave". The only option then was to cause as much embarrassment as possible to one's escort and in this respect, we were spoilt for choice.

51

The less imaginative amongst us would rely heavily on bodily functions to achieve a result. The ancient Bonnie Bun-Bun, for example, had minimal control at the best of times, so a glimpse of a white coat was all it took to produce a steaming pudding or an amber fountain; Miss Isabelle had perfected the projectile vomit at an early stage in her career and didn't hesitate to share the fruits of this finely-honed skill with the vet, the nurse and as many people in the waiting room as possible. A particular triumph was successfully targeting a rather irritating and over-enthusiastic boxer dog who showed signs of wishing to mate with everything in sight including Miss Isabelle's cat carrier.

Bella, or should I say St Petersburg Cloud Princess, adopted a slightly more subtle approach – if grinding one's face against the bars of the carrier can be so termed. Although the journey to the vet's surgery was no more than fifteen minutes, even with the EM's idiosyncratic approach to map reading, Bella managed to arrive looking more like a hairy beetroot than you would imagine possible for a pedigree blue tortoiseshell Persian.

My own technique was to fling myself at the vet as if he or she was my one chance of survival in a cruel world, while displaying abject terror every time the EM so much as looked at me.

Unfortunately, the EM was herself something of an expert when it came to causing embarrassment and the vet's waiting room provided her with all too many opportunities to send us diving under our blankets. Count Lucio took many weeks to recover from the EM's discourse on incontinence. Some hapless pet owner was expressing the view that she wouldn't wish to cope with an incontinent animal when the EM said it could happen to anyone and how would she like to be bumped off because nobody could be bothered to look after her? The woman then made matters worse by giggling and saying she didn't think she'd want to go on in those circumstances, which resulted in the EM going on for another five minutes about the pleasure Bun-Bun still had from stealing everybody's food and walking over other cats' faces. By this time, the Count was fantasising about belonging to the leggy blonde opposite instead of some gobby mushroom with tortoiseshell hair.

CHAPTER NINE

Is There No Limit To My Talents?

It was hardly surprising that I shone in comparison to the challenged creatures in the Special Needs Unit, but gradually I was forced to acknowledge that I really was an exceptionally talented pussycat by any standards. Leaving aside my physical attributes – after all, I was pretty stunning – I had so much charisma that I frightened myself.

Never was this more obvious than when I managed to find the time to visit my adoring public. I almost felt sorry for the EM, trailing along in my wake, desperately trying to get a slice of the action when it was painfully obvious that they were only interested in little old me!

'Tiny's like a little ballet dancer!' they would coo, as I dashed round some far-flung hall after my laser light toy, flinging myself up walls and catching scrunched up paper balls. 'She's *so* pretty – and such a lovely nature!'

Once or twice I almost caught the EM smirking in response to this last remark; indeed, she may even have made some tasteless and inappropriate comment, but luckily my slight deafness protected me from such undeserved cruelty.

I wish I could say that efforts to hone my dancing skills were encouraged, but the EM in particular failed to appreciate my need to practice in the inner hallway. It was perhaps unfortunate that I was at my most acrobatic late at night, when she was stumbling around in her voluminous kangaroo nightdress, clutching a hot water bottle and struggling to maintain her equilibrium as I twirled past her fat legs.

'For Goodness' sake, Tiny!' she would shriek, 'why can't you eat your supper and go to bed like a normal cat? Benjy Boo doesn't keep rushing about, knocking people over!'

Conveniently overlooking the fact that Benjy Boo struggles to put one ginger foot in front of the other unless there's something yummy he needs to stuff down his throat, the EM would try to lure me into my bedroom by dangling Mr Pumpkin, the ever-smiling fishing rod toy, in my face. This inevitably ended in tears when the EM would rush for the door only to find that Mr Pumpkin's elastic had caught on the handle so that the door smacked her in the chops with the force of a left hook from Mike Tyson.

I often reflected on the serene existence of dear Margot Fonteyn compared to my own struggles, but then she probably didn't have as much to laugh at as we did at Tresta Towers. She probably didn't have a friend called "Mr Pumpkin" either.

Not only was I blessed with an overload of talent in the dancing department, but my singing was also coming on a treat. Many of my adoring fans remarked that they had previously imagined deafness would be a disadvantage, but having heard my spirited rendition of *Bridge Over Troubled Water* they could see how mistaken they had been. For a moment I wondered what they meant, but concluded that humans often have difficulty expressing themselves.

Sometimes Bonnie Bun-Bun would join me with her quavery and rather insistent soprano voice, but at the first sighting of a pouch of luxury Kittydins she would abandon our duet to wade fearlessly into her food bowl. I felt very let down by her casual approach to things and asked her if she imagined that Katherine Jenkins would leave Alfie Boe in the lurch if someone wafted a pizza under her nose. Bun-Bun was unconvinced by this and said that Miss Jenkins might not fancy pizza, but she was certain that a cheeseburger with relish would do the trick.

Modesty almost prevents me from recording my prowess in the modern art field, but I realise that I have it within my power to be an inspiration to millions, so needs must.

It happened by accident, as most life-changing events do. I don't mean the sort of accidents that the EM has, of course. That unfortunate trip that resulted in her lying face-down in a sea of cat food was never going to change anybody's life – certainly not for the better, anyway.

My first – and many would say most remarkable – work of art had echoes of a Tate Modern project and proved beyond doubt that quite mundane objects can – in the right paws – create a work both beautiful and challenging. One evening I was flinging Mr Pumpkin about with reckless abandon when I caught my foot on the edge of a dish of cat biscuits. Predictably, the whole lot shot over the wooden floor to form a most moving picture which I instantly realised was in fact a rather witty statement about the meaning of life. I also realised what so many great artists before me must have known – there is a penalty to be paid for being so far ahead of one's time.

It took precisely two minutes for my own particular

penalty to manifest itself when the EM and Bonnie Bun-Bun tottered through on their way to bed and glimpsed my masterpiece.

'Well – that's all we need!' snapped the EM, 'some clumsy cat chucking their food all over the floor!'

As she whisked off to fetch the dustpan and brush, Bun-Bun energetically applied herself to sucking up the biscuits as fast as she could go, so that by the time the EM returned, hardly anything remained apart from gooey pawprints and smears of foul-smelling dribble.

Meanwhile, the EM was continuing to bore everybody rigid with her entries for various poetry competitions, anguishing over whether a comma or a semi-colon would be appropriate – or even a question mark in some circumstances. As the lucky recipient of these ramblings, my day bed being on a pile of books above her desk, I generally tried to nip things in the bud by yawning in an exaggerated manner. This generally had no effect at all, apart from the unfortunate occasion when she happened to notice that my breath was on the pichardy side of fragrant and whisked me off for a scrape and polish.

Having listened to some of the EM's pathetic efforts, I soon realised that I could do so much better. I spent some time wondering what to write about, but in the end gave in to pressure from my admirers and reluctantly composed a rather moving ballad about little old me.

THE BALLAD OF TRIXIE-TRIBBLE

I'm small and striped like a humbug
And I fly around like a bat;
In fact I'm more a pipistrelle –

Than a boring, conventional cat.
I was born with a bit of brain damage
And my head has a slight starboard tilt.
I'm deaf and I'm vague about dirt trays,
But that's just the way that I'm built.
They call me a heat-seeking missile,
And I really do like to have fun.
I love rolling Benjamin over –
As he wobbles along in the sun.
One of my toys is a goldfish
That hangs from a long springy rod.
He's now not looking so golden –
With chips he would pass off as cod.

Once she realised the extent of my formidable poetical powers, the EM abandoned her own pathetic efforts and decided that she would instead embark on a fitness programme – and not before time! Mercifully, the EM decided against the Lycra leggings because she thought we would catch our dear little claws in them. The fact that the population of Woking would have been too terrified to open their curtains or venture into their front gardens didn't seem to weigh in the balance.

Accordingly, with the lengthening of the days, Billy the tricycle was dragged out of hibernation and forced to carry the EM on outings round the estate. Occasionally, they would get up enough speed to overtake an elderly pedestrian, but only if the poor soul had significant mobility problems. Dogs seemed to find this vision of loveliness particularly irresistible, flinging themselves under the tyres and piddling against the wheels in an orgy of excitement.

Interestingly, the EM's fitness plan did not include cutting down on chocolates or El Plonko. In fact, after a sedate ten-minute ride on Billy, she would feel she had burnt up enough calories to put her feet up with the much-played DVD of *Les Miserables,* slurping and munching through every emotional crisis, while repelling Bun-Bun's skinny-pawed insistence on sampling an orange surprise.

Meanwhile, Poor Roger was fully occupied with his photography and on the rare occasions he wasn't struggling to do justice to my feline charms in any number of winsome poses, he would be in the back garden snapping away at the various challenged forms of wildlife that rashly blundered within range. There was great excitement one morning when two huge birds appeared. Benjamin Wobble immediately became extremely "fritted" and tried to hide under his bonking cushion, while Count Lucio and I dribbled with anticipation at the window. Just as Poor Roger had assembled his lenses, the pin-headed pheasants hauled themselves into the wide blue yonder. Their loss was the grey slug's gain, however, as having lugged all his equipment out into the further reaches of the "conservation area", Poor Roger was determined to capture some wildlife in action. Whether the slug measured up in the action department, I will leave you to imagine.

I was always blamed whenever the wildlife failed to oblige. I was accused on various occasions of leering at the woodpecker – a showy, rather noisy bird – and of threatening the fox cubs by holding my ears "in a certain way". Even the EM couldn't accuse me of upsetting the badgers, however. Once old Moonbeam and Brillo had their snouts in the trough, a volcano could have erupted in the next street and they wouldn't have noticed.

Life was pretty exhausting at Tresta Towers, even before the legs fell off my toy chicken and Evie plummeted into the dirt tray from a great height. I began to see the advantages of getting away from it all for a while and decided to browse through the holiday brochures on the EM's desk. There was a ridiculous fuss when she found I'd scrunched them up and piddled on them, but exactly why would I want to go to the Dalmatian Coast? I could feel a clutch of spots popping up at the mere thought of it.

CHAPTER TEN

The Hour Is Always Darkest...

I think it might have been the long dark days that got me down – or possibly the strain of living with tidal waves of incontinence and the ghostly rattling of the drugs trolley twice a day – but as we trundled through January I found myself reflecting on the injustices suffered by cats over the years.

Looking at the heap of fuzzy candyfloss that was St Petersburg Cloud Princess and listening to her snoring I wondered how an army of Persians had ever succeeded in following that self-seeking Darius the Great across the known world. I'm amazed that those poor cats managed to march at all with those knobbly little legs and silly flat faces. As for sneaking up on the Greeks – if they made as much noise as Bella, it's a miracle they ever surprised anybody.

Then there were the witches' cats who had a terrible time. As if it wasn't bad enough having to live with a batty old woman with an unnatural fondness for bats and toads, they were victimised by a half-witted population that had suddenly decided they were evil. This must have been really vexing for the cats who had gone from being worshipped to being very nearly wiped out in the blinking of an eye. I consoled myself with reflecting how cats eventually had the last laugh, even if things weren't too jolly meanwhile. With a drop in the moggy population, the rats were having a non-stop party and spreading their horrible fleas wherever they felt like it. The result? The plague spread across the nation and the NHS was up to its eyes in pustules before it knew what had hit it.

And why that dog was picked to star in *Lassie*, I'll never know. How many children had to wander off and get lost before the casting director began to suspect that Lassie was just in it for the doggy treats? As for *Rin Tin Tin* – any cat would have realised how silly it was to set off with half a dozen soldiers to bandy words with three thousand Cherokees on the other side of the hill. The cat would have sat down, washed its bottom and generally indicated that it would be much more sensible to stay behind the barricades and eat sausages.

Even more blatant discrimination has occurred where a human has had the bare-faced cheek to name something after a cat, but resolutely refused to share any of the fame – or the royalties. To the best of my knowledge, Percy Shaw – the much praised inventor of the Cat's Eye reflecting device which has saved so many human lives – failed lamentably to give any credit to the source of his inspiration. Oh yes – when pressed, he seemed to think he could have been prompted by the sight of a cat's eyes glinting in the headlights as he drove home one night. Not good enough, Percy! Poor old Sooty had been risking life and limb on that road for months before you finally got the message.

Then there was the Cat's Whisker radio. It can't have been any fun for those cats who sacrificed their whiskers so that future generations could tune in to Chris Evans'

Breakfast Show. Imagine getting jammed in a succession of narrow openings for the benefit of idiots who can't eat their toast without a burbling cacophony of travel information and weather reports! No wonder cats have been a bit slow to see the joke. In fact, I can't remember the last time I laughed at a Chris Evans' joke either.

Just as I was feeling that my plans for world domination had come to a grinding halt, I found myself increasingly drawn to Miss Elizabeth, the revenge queen of Tresta Towers. I began to think I may have been a trifle hasty in my assessment of the diminutive matriarch as a bit of a creep and a spy in the camp, having seen the old tart cuddling up to the EM on the sofa every night.

I had always admired the powerful slaps she administered to the boys without any warning and apparently without any reason. Stumpy Malone was a favourite target; he only had to have looked at her three days previously for her to suddenly floor him with a sharp jab – he never saw it coming. Benjamin Wobble, the ginger hot water bottle, was hardly a challenge, but as Elizabeth was fond of pointing out, a good smack could only improve him and helped to keep her slapping muscles in trim. Her most impressive victories, however, were over Count Lucio, who was easily four times as big as our pint-sized heroine and fond of terrorising the rest of the feline population when he had one of his macho turns. He would race up to Elizabeth, confident that she would run, only to find himself felled by a smack in his rather good looking chops.

One of the benefits of this sisterly bonding was that I began to see that there was more than one way of exerting one's supremacy – or, as she put it, "of skinning a human". I'm not being unkind when I say that Miss Elizabeth was not one of life's natural beauties, having been born with very strange hind legs and a short tail with an unbecoming kink at the body end, but I was beginning to appreciate the power of her personality.

This came to the fore when Poor Roger succumbed to a mystery illness and took to his bed. The EM, conscious as always of her reputation as the ideal wife, ignored the groaning and moaning, and carried on with her punishing schedule of girlie lunches and other social engagements that masqueraded as cat care assignments. Only when the patient lapsed into a feverish silence did she begin to think that Poor Roger could actually be quite ill and when he showed no sign of rallying for the weekly meeting of the Camera Club, she was immediately on the phone to the doctor.

A virus was diagnosed and the doctor stressed that the patient should make sure he drank enough. There is no record of this advice ever needing to be given to the EM, needless to say. As the days went by with the EM making a great fuss about how much she'd got to do with Poor Roger wallowing in his bed of pain, Miss Elizabeth began to think that cat-care standards were falling below an acceptable level. Things reached an all-time low at lunch time on Day Four when, instead of freshly opened pouches for our lunch, the EM merely grabbed a fork and poked around at the remains of our breakfast before shoving the dishes back on the floor.

'There we are – lunch is served!' she said, obviously confident that she'd fooled us.

Predictably, Benjamin Wobble lurched forward to vacuum up the food and had to be restrained by a lightening left hook from Elizabeth. Bonnie Bun-Bun was unstoppable, even after several slaps from Lizzie's sharp little white paw, but as Elizabeth remarked later, the most carefully honed plans have to allow for an error rate when they involve an ancient tabby coat-hanger with dementia.

During the afternoon Elizabeth managed to vomit several times and was carted off to the vet, smirking triumphantly, although the EM convinced herself that the smirk was wind and therefore further evidence of indisposition.

A couple of injections later Miss Elizabeth returned and felt strong enough to nibble some lightly poached fish. She also felt strong enough to sit on the EM's chest all evening, breathing *Eau de Coley* into her face in the friendliest way and even managed to tip a glass of El Plonko down the EM's dinosaur jumper without being reprimanded.

Meanwhile, the EM was so distracted by Miss Elizabeth's "turn" that she quite forgot about Poor Roger for hours at a time, leaving the poor soul languishing in the bedroom with a weak orange drink and some cold toast for company. This was in sharp contrast to the devotion shown to Count Lucio over the festive season, when the EM was in and out of the sick room more times than Bonnie Bun-Bun came into the kitchen looking for her lunch. This was not always appreciated by the Count, who complained loudly about the interruptions and constant plumping of pillows. Poor Roger's pillows remained largely unplumped for the duration of his illness, possibly bolstering his determination to emerge from the sickroom at an early stage.

Various friends phoned to ask after Poor Roger and

rang off without ever mentioning him, deflected by the EM's lively account of Miss Elizabeth's health worries. It was only when a second visit to the vet's found its way into the diary along with the dreaded words "blood test?" that Miss Elizabeth began to make sustained progress.

Although my friendship with Miss Elizabeth continued to blossom, I have to say that some of the others were really getting on my nerves. There was a huge row when the EM caught me with a mouthful of ginger fur and accused me of attacking Benjamin Wobble.

'Miss Bully Cat does not live in this house!' she exclaimed, grabbing me and shoving me into my Tiny House. 'I will not have this bad behaviour, Madam! Poor Benjy's really fritted!'

He had it coming! Sneaking up behind me like that and trying to have his wicked way with me, even if his "wicked way" did consist of flattening me and dribbling all over my beautiful tabby fur.

As we edged cautiously into spring, however, things cheered up enormously and I began to see the wisdom of Miss Elizabeth's words. Perhaps we already had achieved world domination and I just hadn't realised. As I looked round me now, I could see evidence of feline superiority even amongst the challenged dollops of Tresta Towers. If it was true that you couldn't judge a book by its cover, or even a sausage by its skin, perhaps Benjy Boo's blank little face concealed a razor-sharp mind more concerned with the origin of the universe than stealing Bun-Bun's supper or bonking his cushion – unlikely though it seemed.

CHAPTER ELEVEN

Cats Behaving Badly

I shall always be grateful to Miss Elizabeth for her help, without which I might still have been trying to raise an army and agonising over what colour uniform would be most becoming. With the realisation that cats were already running things, came a welcome sense of liberation – rather like the EM no doubt experiences when she removes her Marigolds after disinfecting the dirt trays.

I was slightly peeved about all the time I'd wasted on strategic planning, but resolved to make up for lost time by flinging myself into life at the theme park known as Tresta Towers.

Once I started looking at things differently, I noticed that the most unlikely members of my feline family were achieving some pretty remarkable things and felt the first stirrings of something frighteningly close to admiration. Benjamin Wobble, for example, even succeeded in causing a crisis while asleep. Amazingly for one so large, he managed to fall asleep behind a cushion on the sofa, initiating a three hour search of the garden and the woods beyond and sparking off more recriminations and expletives than you would have thought possible on a Sunday afternoon in a quiet cul de sac. The pristine condition of the magazine supplements testified to the extent of the crisis and the chicken had to put up with being roasted at temperatures normally experienced in the centre of an erupting volcano so that dinner could be served before midnight.

When the end of Benjy's ginger tail was at last spotted, twitching languidly across Bonnie Bun-Bun's face, the EM and Poor Roger nearly pulled him apart in their desperation to hug him to their bosoms. Poor Roger rushed around looking, I suspect for a fatted calf to slaughter, and the EM was so thrilled that she quite overlooked the fact that "somebody" had trodden quantities of rancid fox poo into the carpet.

The rather pretty and entirely mad Miss Evie was incensed when she heard about Benjamin's triumph and resolved to show what a cat can achieve when it puts its mind to it. As is the way with felines, Evie let a few weeks go by before she put her plan into practice, so that everybody was feeling relaxed and vaguely confident about the way things were going. Having snoozed away the nights on the sofa for many months, Evie decided that she absolutely must go out at midnight just as a light wind was springing up.

Reluctantly Poor Roger and the EM let her out and instantly regretted doing so. The wind intensified to gale force within minutes of Evie's departure and the heavens opened, so that the badgers' cordon bleu supper resembled soup before it had hit the deck. Severe weather warnings came thick and fast and the back garden soon resembled a scene from *Moby Dick* – particularly when the EM tottered out in her nightdress to beg Evie to come in.

Days went by and the EM and Poor Roger spent long hours in the woods, slithering about in the mud and inflicting serious damage on the trees by stumbling against them. The EM printed out sad little notices which she stuck through neighbours' doors, exhorting them to open up their sheds and garages in case dear little Evie had got shut in.

There was, of course, some entirely innocent amusement to be had when well-meaning people asked the EM if she'd thought of looking in the woods. Another sweet man suggested that Evie might have been eaten by a fox or a badger, or possibly a pterodactyl. The consumption of El Plonko increased dramatically during this stressful period, only to increase even more when Evie sauntered home some five days later with a nonchalant shrug and the implication that everything was somehow the EM's fault.

Stumpy Malone revealed hidden depths when he went and sat on a visitor's lap. In itself this does not sound all that newsworthy, but the subtle significance of this perceived act of treachery was that the footless wonder had never sat on a lap before. The EM and Poor Roger could only stare in disbelief as our hero settled himself down on a stranger's knee, purring his little black heart out and shooting the occasional far from innocent look at his stricken humans. The EM lost no time in recounting this development to Stumpy's Godmother – a close friend who for many months insisted on calling him "Sebastian", but in the end recognised that he lacked the sophistication of dear Lord Coe, or even of Sebastian Flyte's teddy bear – the bear that the EM had spent so many happy hours dribbling over in her *Brideshead Revisited* era.

'I couldn't believe it,' the EM trilled. 'We were just having a glass of wine and a few nibbles and Stumpy emerged from his igloo, looked at Joan and went straight over, climbed up her legs and settled himself down.'

His Godmother must have asked whether Stumpy might have mistaken Joan for the EM.

'No – nothing like me. She's rather glamorous and very slim.'

I pitied the Godmother, desperately casting around for a tactful response. I don't know what she said in the end, but the conversation ended rather suddenly. Possibly she was lucky enough to spot a mad axe murderer wending his way up the drive, or the house was burning down. Either eventuality would have been infinitely preferable to upsetting the EM.

Of course, one often felt the need of an audience rather than wasting one's amusing little party tricks on humans that had basically already capitulated. A steady stream of vulnerable people seemed to totter across the threshold of Tresta Towers – some of them clinging to the assumption that they were visiting a normal household. The EM would always ask people if they had a problem with cats before they embarked on their perilous mission – something she has felt the need to check on since the boiler maintenance man fell to the ground clutching his throat after five minutes in a confined space with Benjamin Wobble.

The reply would usually be along the lines of, 'No – I love cats! I've got two of my own – wouldn't be without them!'

One such visitor was welcomed with tea and cake the other afternoon, only to experience the unnerving sight of Bonnie Bun-Bun accelerating towards her across the sofa. Leaving aside the risk of asphyxiation from that pilchard breath, the visitor was plunged into a spirited disagreement over ownership of the jam sponge which she had planned to wedge in her mouth. With one deft swipe of her emaciated paw, Bun-Bun sent the sponge flying to the ground and swooped on it like an uncoordinated, but very hungry, bird of prey. After a few mouthfuls she realised that she actually didn't like it at all and made vigorous attempts to bury it in the carpet.

With the arrival of an unsullied slice of sponge cake and a few half-hearted apologies, the visitor settled down for a chat, only to be distracted by Miss Whizzy ripping lumps out of an armchair. Pointing shakily at our three-legged friend, she drew the EM's attention to this extremely bad behaviour.

The EM was entranced. 'Yes – isn't it wonderful how well she balances on that single hind leg?' she simpered. 'You are such a clever girl, Whizzy-Woo!'

This misdemeanour was rapidly followed by a sinister "plop" which signified that St Petersburg Cloud Princess had descended from the dining table. If the visitor was surprised when the EM scuttled from the room clutching swathes of kitchen roll, she managed to conceal her emotion with a slightly nervous giggle, before gathering up her belongings and heading for the door. The EM, meanwhile, was mopping up and congratulating our fuzzy little gremlin on a particularly well-formed and productive poo.

'I've been so worried about dear Bella!' she explained as our visitor fled down the path. 'She was a martyr to constipation this time last year and we had to try all sorts of things before we got her sorted out!'

Surprisingly, instead of pleading for more information, the poor woman jumped into her car and roared into the gathering gloom – probably stopping off at the off-licence on the way home.

Nowhere was our feline superiority more conspicuous than in the menu department. During Poor Roger's viral indisposition he would murmur weakly about tasty little dishes that he thought might tempt his jaded appetite.

'Perhaps some chicken in white sauce?' he would venture during one of the EM's rare visits to the sick room, only to be verbally slapped back on the pillows with a brisk, 'I think toast would be best. Easy to digest and very low in fat. You could have half a banana after that, then a weak cup of tea. We'll see how that settles.'

In sharp contrast to this bracing regime was the coaxing approach adopted by the EM during Count Lucio's prolonged and extremely comfortable convalescence. Not only did he have a vast selection of mouth-watering dishes, but they would be spread within easy reach of the patient as he languished on their bed. The result was that the EM and Poor Roger spent their nights not only trying to accommodate Count Lucio's bulky and overheated body, but also doing their best to avoid a precarious arrangement of sardines in tomato sauce and a tempting array of thinly sliced garlic sausage.

It didn't take me long to realise that it wasn't just cats that had achieved superiority over the human race. The badgers exerted formidable power and trashed the garden whenever they felt like it – or whenever their supper wasn't quite up to the mark.

I could have told the EM it was a mistake giving them bananas when Poor Roger finally found the strength to rebel and said he couldn't face another over-ripe lump of slime. Perhaps this could have been more tactfully expressed, but everybody has their breaking point. He paid a dreadful price, of course, with nothing to eat or drink for days. Anyway, the badgers didn't like the look of the bananas one bit and smeared them everywhere you could think of and a few you would struggle to name, including the door of the summerhouse which enraged Miss Whizzy and didn't do a lot for the EM.

I've heard quite a lot about smear campaigns, but I have to admit that the one initiated by those pointy-faced barrage balloons was pretty impressive. When they had finished with the bananas, they rampaged through the borders, ripping out bulbs as fast as they could go, but thoughtfully leaving the clumps of dandelions and thistles which are such a feature here. I quite expected the EM to retaliate with some boiled turnips or yet another failed dessert, but she bent over backwards to please them, making a pile of peanut butter sandwiches and cutting them into dainty triangles – for animals who can bite through a thighbone like it was a lump of congealed porridge!

I had the pheasants down as a couple of airheads, but old Freddie surpassed himself one morning when he flew up out of the bushes just as the EM was tottering back after closing the badger tunnel. Struggling to her feet after an unduly intimate encounter with a birch sapling, the EM was heard to call Freddie some fairly rude names. Within minutes she regretted being so spiteful and rushed out with handfuls of corn for him, 'because he must have had a very bad fright'. Needless to say, old airhead was back in the garden within minutes and yumming back the extra rations. I suspect that men with guns would have held no terrors for him once he'd coped with the EM in her nightdress.

CHAPTER TWELVE

My Charity Work

It was only a short time before I began to realise that with power comes responsibility – something that the EM and Poor Roger have yet to grasp and I for one am jolly pleased they haven't. Not that they have any power, of course, but they do have considerable, if menial, responsibilities and that is just how things should be. Perish the thought that they should wake up one morning and suddenly start craving power! At the first sign of such waywardness, Miss Elizabeth and I would be compelled to take decisive action and I wouldn't rule out draconian measures like diverting the Tesco's wine delivery van or causing a couple of fairly expensive camera lenses to hit the deck. Hopefully, it will never come to that; in fact, one glance at their blank little faces as they struggle with the complexities of the remote control always reassures us.

Being the generous-spirited cat I am, however, I was anxious to give something back to the rather challenged humans at Tresta Towers and spent many happy hours planning all sorts of surprises that would spice up their boring little lives.

I decided to delegate responsibility for anything to do with motoring to Count Lucio. For one thing, I had a lot more important things to concern myself with and also the EM had decided that I wasn't to be allowed out on my own – presumably because she couldn't bear the thought of someone running off with me. Although the Count complained endlessly about having to make time for this activity, I buttered him up by telling him that it was only a cat of his speed and daring that could be trusted with the brake-testing mission. Within a short time, he was putty in my little tabby paws and clamouring to be told what to do.

'Wait until the EM has done all that looking under the car stuff and walked round it about six times, then – once she's backed out into the road and by some fluke is moving forward – shoot out of the bushes and dash in front of the car. Ten points for a squeal of brakes and twenty for getting her to mount the pavement!'

What innocent fun we had watching from the windowsill! And to think of the lives we saved by testing those brakes so rigorously, in all weathers. Quite often after one of the more spectacular pavement-mounting manoeuvres the EM would abandon all thoughts of going out in the car and stumble back indoors, heading for the El Plonko bottle. Proof, if proof were needed, that even if there was nothing wrong with the car, the woman should be kept off the road at all costs.

I realised at an early stage that Benjamin Wobble was not exactly cast in a heroic mould, resembling as he did a fur-covered and over-stuffed beanbag. I tried to engage his attention to discuss what charity work he might be capable of undertaking, but unfortunately once he realised I wasn't interested in a quick bonk he glazed over and was asleep within seconds. In the end I decided to maximise his natural talents – the sleeping, I mean, not the others – by encouraging him to sit down behind the door so that when Poor Roger or the EM came thundering through, damage to the wall by over-vigorous door flinging would be averted by the presence of our porky little doorstop.

We watched *Psycho* the other evening – or some of us did, while the EM cringed irritatingly behind a large cushion, pleading with us to tell her "when it was safe to look". Resisting the urge to poke her eyes out because this would not have fitted with my newly acquired charitable persona, I concentrated instead on thinking about how I could help her overcome this nervousness.

Next time she disappeared into the shower, I waited until she was well into her *Abba* repertoire before fighting my way through the plastic curtain and leaping at the sponge. If only she had seen that this was the very therapy she needed to overcome all those irrational fears about shower curtains! In the confusion, I caught my dear little claws in her leg and had a real struggle to extract them with her flailing about and screaming her head off. There was blood everywhere, including on my fur. I learned a tough lesson that day: some people are beyond help and the EM appeared to be one of them.

When I related this sorry tale to Miss Elizabeth, she put her sharp little head on one side and stared at me. For a moment I thought she was mocking my (very slight) head tilt and was about to clock her one, realising just in time that she was about to confide in a sisterly manner. Apparently, when Miss Elizabeth was a few months old, she noticed that the EM had an entirely irrational fear of worms and made it her business to help her overcome it – in a caring way, naturally.

The therapy consisted of finding a nice lively worm,

bringing it indoors and leaving it for the EM to find. Nothing wrong with that, you would think, but the ungrateful woman just screamed her head off and phoned any number of unfortunate neighbours who would have to turf out at the most inconvenient times to remove Mr Wriggly from the premises. I should point out that this was in the pre-Poor Roger era, when the EM's totally irrational behaviour had to be shared around the neighbourhood instead of becoming a full-time job for one person.

Unsurprisingly, it was the ancient tabby coat-hanger who took control of any food-related tasks. No sooner had the EM lurched back from the shops, than Bonnie Bun-Bun would stagger into the kitchen to supervise the unpacking process. Deaf as the proverbial post, Bun-Bun said that she experienced a strange vibration in her whiskers in the presence of food and, having seen her sit bolt upright on the sofa when some frozen fishcakes crossed the threshold recently, I saw no reason to doubt her.

Such is the superiority of the feline brain that even Bun-Bun, struggling as she did with advanced dementia, was streets ahead of the EM when it came to sorting out the shopping. While the EM was still rabbiting on about the child who stuck his finger in the very cream cake she was planning to buy and about the scandalous absence of special offers in the El Plonko department, Bun-Bun was rooting through the bags with a diligence that many airport staff could learn from.

All the boring and inedible things were rejected with a powerful swipe of her skinny old paw, so that she could concentrate on the more promising items like thinly sliced ham and – a particular favourite – apricot yoghurt. Once she had located these delicacies, Bun-Bun drew heavily upon her long years of experience and illustrated how the EM could save time by leaving out an entirely superfluous stage in the process. Instead of fiddling about putting them away in the fridge, the ham and yoghurt could be slapped straight on to Bun-Bun's plate. Over the course of a year, Bun-Bun calculated that this would save some three weeks of pointless human activity – time that could be so much more usefully spent cooking chickens and coley steaks.

Sparing no effort, Bun-Bun was also touchingly keen to help with the cooking, but had to be restrained when she showed a worrying determination to climb into the red hot oven. In the end, she had to settle for a monitoring role, taking up her position by the oven door and fighting off all-comers until finally overwhelmed by weariness and the smell of roasting chicken.

Of course, cats have always relished a challenge, but for a long time I had struggled to think of St Petersburg Cloud Princess as a cat, bearing in mind her close resemblance to a cross between a mop and a particularly shapeless lump of candyfloss. I was forced to revise my opinion after her spectacular performance following the EM's speech about it being difficult to see when the kitchen floor required cleaning.

Our favourite Persian has always subscribed to the view that dirt trays are unhygienic, making a point of piddling on the floor, but nothing had prepared any of us for the shimmering amber lake that spread across the kitchen that morning, seeping under cupboards and threatening to sabotage every electrical appliance in the place.

The EM's gratitude was a trifle restrained. 'Well, that's a big help, that is!' she remarked, with just the faintest hint of sarcasm.

Within minutes the Marigolds were donned and the EM was up to her armpits in disinfectant and froth. Partial deconstruction of the kitchen followed, and the whole operation took so long that lunch was rather late. On balance, we decided not to make too much of that.

If all this activity sounds a bit on the earnest side, I must point out that as well as my invaluable work in schools and other worthy institutions, I spared no effort to provide EM and Poor Roger with some much-needed exercise and recreation. It did my heart good to see the EM scampering around after Mr Pumpkin and my pink clockwork mouse! She always pretended that she was too tired, but once she got going I could tell she enjoyed it – and never more than at one in the morning.

Stumpy Malone took responsibility for making sure Poor Roger didn't fall into the trap of oversleeping by sitting on the pillow for hours, waiting for that first twitch of the covers. This would galvanise the footless one into frenzied action, pouncing at the covers and snatching them away from Poor Roger's recumbent form. We would hear the muffled cries of delight as the game got going, with Poor Roger entering into the spirit of things by pretending to be cross.

'Go away, you little bugger!' he would shout, 'you've scratched my lip! Leave me alone!'

Leaving aside the punishing schedule that means on some days I struggle to snatch twenty-three hours' sleep, I'm pleased I came to Tresta Towers. Most of us like to feel needed and there's no doubt that I'm needed here – one glance at the EM, Poor Roger and the challenged felines in the Residents' Lounge would convince anybody.

It's obviously only a matter of time before I receive the recognition I deserve in the New Year's Honours List and I'm already wondering whether any of the collars in my extensive wardrobe would be up to the challenge. On balance I think not and the same probably applies to the EM and Poor Roger, who would no doubt insist on accompanying me and disgracing themselves long before we got to the canapés.

Still, in the spirit of charity I would have to let them come along with a view to ditching them at an early stage in the proceedings. That way I'd be able to spend some quality time with Royalty without the worry of the EM spilling El Plonko down her front or Poor Roger tripping over his tripod.

IN CASE YOU WONDERED

There may be readers who are worrying about the possible stress inflicted on Tiny Trixie-Tribble by taking her to schools and other venues when I've been invited to do a talk about cats and the work of Cats Protection.

I should explain that this is not something I did without very careful consideration, taking account of Tiny's unique characteristics and disabilities (although she would never think of them as that!). I have had many cats over the years and Tiny is the first one to fit the bill – and to enjoy every minute!

Tiny isn't completely deaf, but her hearing is sufficiently impaired to make it dangerous for her to roam freely. The noise of the vacuum cleaner fails to wake her, for example, although the rest of the cats cannot bear the noise it makes – thus providing me with the perfect excuse for rarely tackling the tumbleweed drifts of fur that waft across the cluttered floors of Tresta Towers. Tiny's inability to hear this sort of noise appears to help when it comes to travelling in the car; she seems totally relaxed in her carrier on the back seat and has never indulged in the projectile vomiting and worse that can make car journeys with cats such a nightmare for the cats and their humans.

The deafness helps too when small children become excited and their shrill voices have the adults present wishing they could adjust the volume control. Many cats are nervous of small children because of the suddenness and pitch of their voices – this is a bit unfair when you consider the noise that cats can make when they feel like it, but cats have never pretended that their version of logic is the same as ours!

The other factor is Tiny's brain damage, which appears to make her completely fearless in any situation. This does, of course, have its disadvantages in that she would think nothing of bouncing up to a rabid dog or a hungry fox. The great plus, however, is that Tiny is completely at ease in large gatherings and plays to the gallery by chasing her toys and sitting on laps, to the great delight of children of all ages.

She is a wonderful ambassador for cats and for pets generally, often winning over children who have no direct experience of animals by providing a soft and playful presence in a totally safe environment. I have been deeply moved on many occasions to see small children relax in her presence after an initially nervous response and extend a small hand to stroke her.

The additional benefit, of course, is that it doesn't really matter too much what I'm rambling on about because Tiny is the undisputed star of the show.